Magnifice...

A Read-Aloud Book to Encourage Children with Dyslexia.

Written by Andra Harris

Illustrated by Julie Wells

Garden Bench Publications
Livermore, CA

Magnificent Meg

A Read-Aloud Book to Encourage Children with Dyslexia

Illustrated by Julie Wells

Hardback ISBN: 978-1-7352515-2-3
Paperback ISBN: 978-1-7352515-1-6
eBook ISBN: 978-1-7352515-0-9

Library of Congress Control Number: 2020912524

Garden Bench Publications
Livermore, CA

Dedicated to my two daughters who do
hard things every day and don't give up.
I'm incredibly blessed to be your Momma.

Hi! I'm Meg. I'm a SUPER kid. I am smart, funny, talented, thoughtful, and kind.

I love to cook,

paint,

and build
with Legos.

I love to play outside with my sister.
We catch frogs and plant flowers.

We draw with chalk
on the sidewalk

and fill the bird
feeder outside
our window.

I love to learn. I watch birds as they
build their nests and protect their eggs.

I look at things through
a magnifying glass

and make volcanoes
with baking soda
and vinegar.

I help my parents fold laundry, vacuum,
clean my room, and set the table.
I love being a helper.
We make a great team.

I love stories. I especially love it when my parents read to us at bedtime.

On Saturdays I get to watch cartoons or play video games in the morning, but I don't do it for too long because it's not good for me.

In the afternoon, I ride my bike and play with my sister.

On school days, I try to focus and learn a lot. I want to learn so that I can do great things when I grow up, like be an architect. Some things are difficult, like reading and spelling, but I try my best.

If I am reading a new book for the first time and there are lots of pages, I feel scared.

If the pages in my book have a lot of words on them, I feel nervous. It looks like all of the letters run together.

I don't like to read in front of other people. If I can't read a word, or if I mix up the sounds, I feel embarrassed.

When I am tired or sick, reading is even harder. Sometimes I need to take a short break. Other times, my parents help by reading my homework questions aloud for me. They say reading will get easier if I don't give up. They say they're proud of me for doing hard things.

Sometimes it seems like reading is easy for other kids. But reading is hard for a lot of people, not just me.

EVERYONE

has something that's hard for them.

When it's time to do school work, I do reading first. I warm up by reading my sight word flashcards. It's best to do hard things first, before I get too tired.

When I read a page, I use a paper to cover all the lines except the one I am reading. I read one line at a time.

When I see a new word, I cover up the first part, which my teacher calls the prefix.

Misspelled

I also cover up the last part, which my teacher calls the suffix. That makes big words look a lot smaller.

The root word of this one is SPELL.

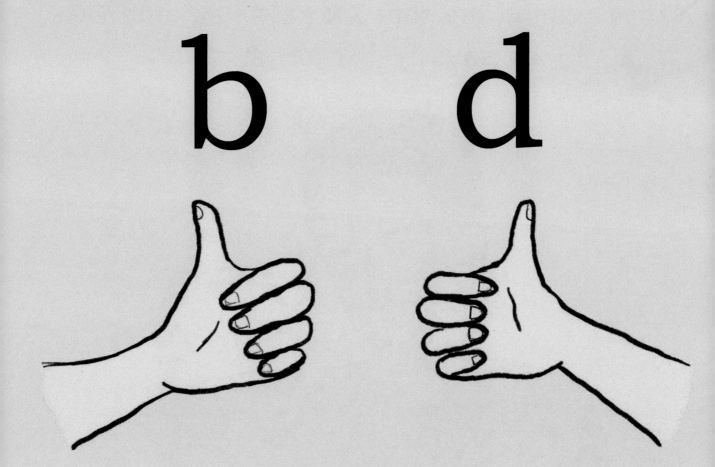

Some letters look confusing to me, like "b" and "d." They are very hard for me to read and write because they look like twins. I hold up my left hand with my thumb up. That helps me remember what "b" looks like. The other hand looks like "d."

My parents help me with super hard words. We sound them out, one syllable at a time. They remind me that AR says "är" and DGE says "j" if I forget.

After I have read a few lines, I feel really proud of myself. Sometimes, before I know it, I have read three whole pages. When I finish a chapter, I am so happy. I feel like a champ!

When I finish a whole book, I feel like I have won an Olympic medal. It feels amazing! All of my hard work is worth it.

Reading may be hard, but I won't give up.
I want to be an architect or a veterinarian
someday. I know I can do it!

Each day I can read new words, and each year I can read bigger books. I am smart. I am strong. I am brave. I am determined.

I can do hard things.

SO

CAN

YOU!

I am a super kid.

AND

SO

ARE

YOU.

Conversation Starters

1. What are your talents and favorite subjects?

2. What are your best character qualities?

The things you said for #1 and #2 are the things that make you **Magnificent!**

3. What things are hard for you to do?

4. How do you feel when you need to read a new book and it looks big?

5. Tell about a time that you worked hard and didn't give up.

6. What is something that used to be hard for you, but now it's easier?

7. What helps you feel better when you are sad, tired, or frustrated?

8. What do you dream of becoming when you grow up?

9. What can you do this week to work toward your dream?

10. What makes you feel like a champ?

Notes to Parents

*When children struggle with reading, they are most likely feeling a great deal of anxiety at school. They need your encouragement, affection, and affirmation to reduce their stress. They need to hear you say, "I'm proud of you for trying your best," "I am impressed by your hard work and determination," "I'm here for you whenever you need help," and "You can do it!"

*Sometimes you may feel like your child is being lazy or not giving their best effort. Your child needs you to be patient. If you have taught them 100 times the correct way to write "b" and "d" and they are still writing them backwards, patiently keep looking for new "tricks" to help them remember. Be the safe, positive encourager that they need.

*Have your child tested to find out the cause of their reading struggles. Be sure to ask testers if they will test for dyslexia.

*For children with dyslexia, a multi-sensory, Orton-Gillingham-based program is the best method for them to learn how to read. To find out more information about dyslexia and Orton-Gillingham systems, visit www.dys-add.com and www.BartonReading.com.

*Reading in front of peers can be humiliating. Ask your child's teacher not to call on your child to read in front of the class unless your child volunteers.

*Children with reading struggles may sometimes feel like giving up. They need your reassurance that in time, with the right methods, reading will get easier. They just need to learn in a different way. Tell them stories about subjects or activities that were hard for you when you were younger. Children need to know that they are not alone.

*School can be exhausting for children with dyslexia. Give them breaks and try to finish reading assignments early in the afternoon before they are too tired.

*Help your child discover their strengths. Music, art, sports, building projects, cooking, community service, debate, drama, etc., are activities in which they may excel. Once they discover their strengths, their confidence will grow.

*Ask your child what they would like to do when they grow up. Encourage them to dream. School isn't just about doing assignments—it's about learning things that will prepare them for the future.

*Reading books aloud to your children is a wonderful way to bond together while keeping the love of story alive. It will also fill their minds with rich vocabulary and good sentence structure, which will help them to become excellent writers.

*Do fun things with your child and work on projects together. Children need to know that reading is just one piece of life; they need reassurance of your love and a break from the stress of school. Let them know that you are their number one fan.

About the Author

Andra Harris has been a teacher for over 20 years and has tutored children with dyslexia for 16 years using the Barton Reading & Spelling System. She loves watching children learn, grow, smile, and achieve their goals. Andra wants to encourage all struggling young readers not to give up, and wants parents to know that they play an important role in helping their child succeed. Andra and her husband live in Northern California and have five children. Find out more about Andra's work at andraharris.com and follow her on Instagram @andralynharris.

About the Illustrator

Julie Wells is a well-loved children's book illustrator and designer. Her lively and innocent designs possess a magical flair that reminds one of the beauty of childhood. She is best known for the joyful simplicity of her emotive faces. After attending a private Liberal Arts college nestled in the Shenandoah Valley and earning her Bachelor of Arts in English Literature, Julie began promoting her professional freelance business. She now resides in Virginia, working as a remote illustrator for Orange Hat Publishing and operating Julie Wells Illustration from her home-based studio. She has illustrated six children's books.

Acknowledgments

Thank you to my husband and children, for your support and encouragement while I wrote this book. Thank you to Cheryl, Nan, Roz, and Karen, the members of my writers group, who have proofread my manuscript countless times. Thank you to Linda, Donna, Tara-Leigh, Chris, Beth, Aimee, Melinda, Judy, Janelle, and Sharon for your friendship and invaluable feedback.

Meg wants to hear what makes YOU magnificent. Email a picture of you holding your Magnificent Meg book to MagnificentMegsFriends@gmail.com. Tell her 2-3 character qualities or talents that make you a magnificent kid. Every week a new photo will be featured on Instagram @magnificentmegsfriends and on Facebook. Follow Magnificent Meg's Friends to read inspirational stories of kids like you!

Manufactured by Amazon.ca
Bolton, ON

26430774R00026